Activity Manual to Accompany

▬ Introduction to ▬

TECHNOLOGY

With activities contributed by:

Dennis Karwatka
Morehead State University
Morehead, Kentucky

Charles H. Peteshel
East Fairmont High School
Fairmont, West Virginia

Gary Fisher
Newton High School
Pleasant Hill, Ohio

Dan Fouts
Cascade Junior High School
Bend, Oregon

James Smallwood
Morehead State University
Morehead, Kentucky

Eric Bergh
Ochoa Junior High School
Hayward, California

WEST PUBLISHING COMPANY

ST. PAUL   NEW YORK   LOS ANGELES   SAN FRANCISCO

Production, Prepress, Printing and Binding by West Publishing Company.

COPYRIGHT © 1993 by   WEST PUBLISHING CO.
610 Opperman Drive
P.O. Box 64526
St. Paul, MN 55164–0526

ISBN 0–314–00765–2

TABLE OF CONTENTS

ENERGY

BIOTECHNOLOGY

PREFACE

This Activity Manual contains reproducible activities that both complement and supplement *Introduction to Technology*. The activities are designed to help your students develop problem-solving and critical thinking skills. They are divided into five categories which correlate to the text. Those categories are:

Communication
Production
Transportation
Energy
Biotechnology

The activities are written at various ability levels. Many include challenging and complex step-by-step or problem-solving techniques and involve the use of various tools and procedures. Others are designed so that students of any ability level will achieve some degree of success. Those activities are:

Logo Design
Drawing Features
Floor Plan
"Can" This Idea
Individual vs. Mass Production
All Bent Out of Shape
World's Tallest Golf Tee
Cut-It-Out!
The Throwaway Throne
Airplane Flight Control Activity
Wings and Things

We hope these activities will present relevant learning experiences for your students. In order to save time, you may photocopy the activities or, if you prefer, extra copies of the manual are available for purchase from the publisher.

DAY OF THE WEEK
Submitted by Dennis Karwatka

Note to Students: Please read the following activity completely through before starting to work. There are some helpful hints in the "What Did You Learn? " section.

DID YOU KNOW...?

There are about 200 computer programming languages but the one named BASIC is the most popular. The letters stand for Beginner's All-purpose Symbolic Instruction Code. It was developed by John Kemeny and Thomas Kurtz and first used in 1964.

BASIC is easier than many other computer languages because it uses some ordinary words and symbols. For example, to multiply and divide three numbers you might write "(3 x 8)/6 = ?" on a piece of paper. In BASIC, you could type two lines on a computer, numbering each line:

```
1     X = (3*8)/6
2     Print X
```

Each numbered line is a **command**. If you then typed **RUN** and pressed the **<ENTER>** key, you would see the number 4 on the computer screen.

A PROBLEM TO SOLVE

Do you know on what day of the week you were born? On what day of the week Independence Day fell in 1776? On what day of the week January 1, 2000 will fall? By correctly typing, saving, and running the following computer program, you can quickly find out.

The program determines the day of the week for all future dates and for any past date in American history since 1752. The United

States adopted a new calendar in 1752 called the Gregorian calendar. You can learn more about the fascinating story of calendars by looking up *calendar* or *Gregorian calendar* in an encyclopedia.

RESOURCES YOU WILL NEED

- any computer (some require a special BASIC program such as GWBASIC, BASICA, or BASIC XL)
- a floppy disk to save the program

A PROCEDURE TO FOLLOW

1. With many computers, the BASIC language doesn't automatically load into the machine when you turn it on. Ask your teacher how to load BASIC into your computer.
2. This program is a type sometimes called *plain vanilla*. That means it has no complicated commands and will operate with practically all computers. If you type the commands *exactly* as shown, the program will probably run on your computer.
3. Type each of the commands shown below. Press the **<ENTER>** key at the end of each line.

```
 10    CLS
 20    DIM A$(10), M$(10), N$(10), Y(4)
 30    PRINT
 40    PRINT "WHAT DAY OF THE WEEK?"
 50    PRINT
 60    PRINT "DETERMINE THE DAY OF THE WEEK"
 70    PRINT "FOR ANY DATE IN AMERICAN HISTORY SINCE"
 80    PRINT "THE AMERICAN ADOPTION OF THE"
 90    PRINT "GREGORIAN CALENDAR IN 1752."
100    PRINT
110    PRINT "YEAR OF INTEREST (FOUR DIGITS) ";
120    INPUT Y
130    C=INT(Y/100)
```

```
140    B=Y-C*100
150    PRINT "MONTH IN   ";Y;" (SPELL OUT) ";
160    INPUT M$
170    IF M$="JANUARY" THEN M=11: B=B-1: GOTO 300
180    IF M$="FEBRUARY" THEN M=12: B=B-1: GOTO 300
190    IF M$="MARCH" THEN M=1: GOTO 300
200    IF M$="APRIL" THEN M=2: GOTO 300
210    IF M$="MAY" THEN M=3: GOTO 300
220    IF M$="JUNE" THEN M=4: GOTO 300
230    IF M$="JULY" THEN M=5: GOTO 300
240    IF M$="AUGUST" THEN M=6: GOTO 300
250    IF M$="SEPTEMBER" THEN M=7: GOTO 300
260    IF M$="OCTOBER" THEN M=8: GOTO 300
270    IF M$="NOVEMBER" THEN M=9: GOTO 300
280    IF M$="DECEMBER" THEN M=10: GOTO 300
290    PRINT "THERE IS NO SUCH MONTH AS  ";M$: GOTO 150
300    PRINT "DATE IN   ";M$;"  ";
310    INPUT R
320    IF R<1 OR R>31 THEN GOTO 300
330    D=R+INT(2.6*M-0.2)-2*C+B+INT(C/4)+INT(B/4)
340    D=D/7
350    X=D-INT(D)
360    P=INT(X*10)
370    IF P=0 THEN N$="SUNDAY": GOTO 450
380    IF P=1 THEN N$="MONDAY": GOTO 450
390    IF P=2 THEN N$="TUESDAY": GOTO 450
400    IF P=4 THEN N$="WEDNESDAY": GOTO 450
410    IF P=5 THEN N$="THURSDAY": GOTO 450
420    IF P=7 THEN N$="FRIDAY": GOTO 450
430    IF P=8 THEN N$="SATURDAY": GOTO 450
440    PRINT
450    PRINT R;"  ";M$;"  ";Y;" FELL ON A  ";N$;"."
460    PRINT
470    PRINT "ANOTHER RUN (Y/N)";
480    INPUT A$
490    IF A$="Y" THEN GOTO 10
```

```
500   CLS
510   PRINT
520   PRINT "I WAS PLEASED TO BE ABLE TO ASSIST YOU."
```

4.   Use your computer's save command to store the program on your floppy disk. Usually, you can type SAVE "DAYOFWK" and press the **<ENTER>** key. Check with your teacher to be sure.

5.   Run the program and answer the questions as they appear on the screen. Answering questions to solve a problem is what makes a computer *user friendly*. To run the program, you can usually type **RUN** and press the **<ENTER>** key. Check with your teacher to be sure.

WHAT DID YOU LEARN?

Computers follow very precise commands. What may seem like a minor error to you might be a serious error to a computer. It was quite important to type the commands *exactly* as shown. Did you ever see words like "syntax error" on the screen? If you did, that meant the computer didn't understand what you wanted it to do. *Syntax* means a proper arrangement of words or symbols. For example, you would make a syntax error if you left out the multiplication symbol (*) in line 140 and typed B=Y-C100. A computer is very "trusting" and will do exactly as it is told. It does not know if you have typed in the wrong information.

Did you have to *debug* your program? In computer terms, debug means to remove errors. For example, suppose at line 450 you had accidentally typed "445". The computer would accept the command when you typed it because you made no syntax errors. However, the program would not run. Several commands say GOTO 450. If the computer cannot find line 450 during the run, it will stop and let you know.

By the way, on what day of the week was July 4, 1776?

4

TECHNOLOGY TIMELINE
Submitted by Jim Smallwood

DID YOU KNOW...?

History plays an important role in the development of technology. Many of the technologies you know today have evolved throughout the twentieth century. Computer, automotive, and air travel technologies are just a few examples.

Inventors and scientists learn many things by studying these historical technological developments. They learn from the successes and failures, and they learn about sociological and environmental impacts. Much of this knowledge can be used to develop better products, improve processes, and create technologies that will benefit the human race.

AN ACTIVITY TO COMPLETE

In this activity you will develop and display an expanded technological timeline. You will study a technology and track the development throughout history to the present time. You will learn how certain time periods and events may have affected technological development. For example, how did World War II affect the development of air travel or atomic research?

RESOURCES YOU WILL NEED

- rope - to be used for hanging the poster board
- poster board
- paper clips or string
- hole punch

A PROCEDURE TO FOLLOW

1. You will be working in small groups of 2-3 students.
2. Choose topic and time period provided by your teacher. You may choose certain time periods (i.e., 1945-1955, 1956-1965, and so on) or a different topic (i.e., air travel or long distance communication).
3. Research your topic and develop a technological timeline following the format given by your teacher. Record the information on the poster board. Use your creativity and artistic expression!
4. Upon completion, present your discoveries to the class in a formal presentation. Display the posters on the timeline in chronological order for all students to study. Do this by hanging the poster on the rope using paper clips or string. To save space, the rope can be attached to two different points on the ceiling, allowing the posters to hang down for easy reading.

WHAT DID YOU LEARN?

1. What is the importance of understanding the historical development of a particular technology?

   _____

   _____

   _____

2. How do events such as war, disaster, and the changing environment affect technological development?

   _____

   _____

   _____

   _____

3. Why have there been so many technological developments during the twentieth century, as compared to previous centuries?

_____

_____

_____

_____

TEAMBUILDING

Submitted by Jim Smallwood

Note to Teachers: *The article "Cooperative Learning in the Technology Classroom" in the Teacher's Manual will provide important background information for this activity. This activity can last for a few class periods or take several days to complete.*

DID YOU KNOW...?

The United States may be experiencing one of the most important changes in the workplace since the Industrial Revolution. This change involves a transformation from the traditional style of management in which decisions are made by the managers, to a relationship that attempts to involve all employees in the decision-making process.

Such a change makes it necessary for employees to develop the skills and attitudes needed to make decisions with other employees. Skills such as problem solving, communication, teambuilding, and group process are a few of the skills that are necessary. The objective of this activity is to help you develop some of these important characteristics.

AN ACTIVITY TO COMPLETE

This activity simulates an employee team in a problem-solving situation. You will have an opportunity to discuss, investigate, and develop a team solution to a problem. Finally, you will have an opportunity to present your solution to the rest of the class.

RESOURCES YOU WILL NEED

The following guidelines will help as you work in teams to develop a solution to a problem.

A. Problem-Solving Method

Step 1— Identify the problem.

Step 2— Define the problem carefully and completely.

Step 3— Investigate the problem (research possible solutions, collect data and facts).

Step 4— Analyze the problem (brainstorm possible solutions).

Step 5— Choose and implement a solution (the team should select the most promising solution).

Step 6— Evaluate the end result.

B. Guidelines for Brainstorming

- Generate a large number of ideas.
- Be sure to record all ideas.
- Free-wheeling is encouraged.
- Assume that everything is possible.
- Encourage everyone to participate.
- Don't make judgments, don't give negative feedback.
- At this point, quantity of ideas is better than quality.

C. Characteristics of a Good Team Member

- Works for consensus (agreement)
- Involves others in the decision-making process
- Trusts, supports, and has genuine concern for other team members
- Listens carefully to other ideas
- Respects and is tolerant of individual differences
- Acknowledges and works through conflict (disagreements) openly
- Considers the new ideas and suggestions of others
- Understands and is committed to team objectives

A PROCEDURE TO FOLLOW

1. Discuss with your teacher and class the importance of teamwork and the information on problem solving, brainstorming, and being a good team member.
2. Your teacher will divide the class into teams of 6-12 students.
3. Appoint or elect a team captain to oversee the team effort and a recorder to write down ideas.
4. Your teacher will give you a problem or situation that requires a team effort for a solution.
5. Follow the procedure of the problem-solving method to arrive at a solution to your problem.
6. As a team, write and present a report on your solution to the class.

WHAT DID YOU LEARN?

1. What characteristics are necessary for being a good team member?

_____

_____

_____

2. How can everyone be a contributing member in a team situation if encouraged and allowed?

_____

_____

_____

3. How important is the team concept in solving problems?

_____

_____

_____

4. What are some of the guidelines for brainstorming?

_____

_____

_____

Name_____ Date_____ Period_____

SILK SCREEN PRINTING

Submitted by Eric Bergh

DID YOU KNOW...?

Did you ever wonder how companies get those pictures of your favorite band or team logo onto your T-shirt? One method is to silk screen the image. Silk screen printing is a method that uses a special stencil, with the picture to be printed, to let the ink go just where the picture will be. The process is the same for making one T-shirt or hundreds.

Until recently, the making of silk screens was a very time-consuming process that required a skilled artist to trace the design onto a thin masking material and then carefully cut away the design with a razor blade. Today, using the computer and thermal silk screens, you can do the same thing quickly and easily! In this activity, you will design, create, and print a silk screen T-shirt or poster. It will take you only about an hour to do what used to take someone many hours of painstaking work.

A PROBLEM TO SOLVE

Using the computer, design a T-shirt silk screen that includes a graphic and text and use it to produce a thermal silk-screened T-shirt or poster.

RESOURCES YOU WILL NEED

- computer (Macintosh™, Apple II™, IBM™, etc.)
- laser printer (or dot matrix printer with access to a copy machine
- white paper for the printer
- Thermofax™ or transparency maker
- Paint or Draw software
- graphic "clip art" software
- thermal silk screen—9" x 11-1/2"
- thermal silk screen frame, plastic—10" x 12"
- double-sided tape
- textile inks of appropriate colors, water soluble, about 1 tablespoon per image
- rubber-edged squeegee
- plastic spatula or spoon for placing ink on screen
- paper towels for cleanup
- steam iron, set to cotton, for making ink permanent
- T-shirt, all cotton or 50/50 cotton and polyester, or construction paper, 9" x 12", assorted colors, for making a poster instead

A PROCEDURE TO FOLLOW

1. Your first task is to choose a graphic for your T-shirt! Look at the available graphics, either printed out or by loading the software into the computer to view the possible choices. If you cannot find anything you like, you may choose to draw your own graphic using Paint or Draw software. When you have the graphic you want, save it to disk.
2. On scratch paper, sketch the design of your T-shirt using the graphic you have chosen. You should consider the following design ideas.

- Keep the design simple and uncluttered. T-shirt pictures have more visual impact if they stand out clearly and don't have a lot of fine details.
- A brief caption (a catchy phrase, group name, etc.) helps set the feeling of the picture. Use large, bold lettering. It should "scan," or read, quickly and easily.
- Most designs are centered horizontally and vertically on T-shirts, but consider asymetrical designs. Often, moving a picture off-center or diagonally can add interest and impact.

3. Once you have decided on a design, show the sketch to your teacher to get some feedback and an OK to go ahead.

4. Load the Paint or Draw software into the computer and open up the graphic you saved. Follow your sketch in positioning the graphic and adding text. Don't be afraid to experiment with changing sizes and positions. You can alter them until the design looks just right! Then, SAVE IT!

5. Print out your design on WHITE paper. If you used a dot matrix printer, you will need to have a copy made using a copy machine. The black toner of the copier will make a clearer image on the thermal silk screen.

6. Have your teacher help you assemble the thermal silk screen and your printed design. The two will be fed into the Thermofax™ set at a medium high heat, which will transfer the image to the silk screen. NOTE: Whatever was BLACK on your design, will become a hole in the masking of the silk screen. Therefore, what is black on your design will be where the ink is placed on the T-shirt!

7. Apply the double-sided tape to the inside of the silk screen frame. Make sure it is firmly pressed in place. Loose tape will allow ink to leak through and may spoil the printing.

8. Carefully separate the thermal silk screen from the printed design. You should be able to see the image of the design on the screen when it is held up to the light. Ask the teacher or a helper to hold the silk screen frame while you carefully lower the silk screen FACE DOWN onto the tape. Press down the corners of one end and stretch the screen as you lay it over the rest of the tape. The

screen should end up tight and smooth. Firmly rub down the screen against the tape.

9. Place SEVERAL layers of paper towel inside the T-shirt, underneath the place where the design will go. Lay the shirt out on a table and smooth out the T-shirt carefully. It must be flat. If needed, carefully iron it flat. (If you are going to make a paper poster instead, lay down the construction paper on the table.) Lay the silk screen frame FACE UP on the T-shirt and position it where you want the design.

10. Open the jar of ink you want to use and scoop out a small amount with a plastic spatula or spoon and place the ink in a line on the screen, below the image. Have a helper hold the silk screen frame steady on the shirt and pick up the rubber-edged squeegee. Hold the squeegee in both hands, with your thumbs under the wood handle and fingers extending out on the top side. Press the squeegee down onto the screen, in the ink, holding the squeegee at a 45° angle. Slowly pull the squeegee toward you, pressing down hard enough to flex the rubber of the squeegee. Try to cover the entire design in one pull.

11. CAREFULLY lift off the silk screen frame, lifting from one end. Don't touch the ink on the shirt! When the ink dries, it can be made permanent by laying the shirt on paper towels and ironing the design from the inside of the T-shirt with an iron set on "cotton."

12. Clean up the screen by washing it in the sink, running water across the screen, then gently wiping it with a wet paper towel as the water flows over it. Do this to BOTH sides—you need to force the ink out of the holes in the screen. If you will be using the screen again leave it on the frame; otherwise, carefully pull it off the frame and peel/rub off the tape from the frame.

WHAT DID YOU LEARN?

1. What elements of design should be considered when developing your sketch?

_____

_____

_____

2. How is the printed computer graphic transformed into a silk screen?

_____

_____

_____

3. What must be done to make the water soluble ink become permanent?

_____

_____

_____

4. What could you change in this activity to make it easier to print 12 T-shirts with the same design?

_____

_____

_____

5. How could you use this project to raise money for a school club? What expenses would you need to plan for? How much labor (working time) would you need to plan for?

_____

_____

_____

_____

DESIGN A WRENCH
Submitted by Charles H. Peteshel

DID YOU KNOW...?

You have probably heard the expression "A picture is worth a thousand words." Often, it is much easier to describe an object with a picture that it is to describe it with words.

Technical drawings enable architects, engineers, technicians, and tradespeople to describe the size, shape, and structure of complex objects.

Tools are often the subjects of technical drawings. When a tool is being created, technical drawings are used to describe the tool in detail to the person who will be making it.

Sometimes tools are no longer available. When that happens, it is necessary to re-create the tool.

A PROBLEM TO SOLVE

Bill Rosin has just turned 16 years of age and has met all requirements necessary to apply for a West Virginia driver's license. As a reward for consistently being on the honor roll at school and working at all of the chores assigned at home, his parents have given him an antique 1936 Ford convertible.

He must do some work on the car under the supervision of his older brother, Sam, who is a certified mechanic. The brakes on this car are adjusted with a special wrench that is no longer available.

You will design and draw the wrench, adding dimensions in the appropriate places.

Drawing tools such as
- pencil or pen
- graph paper
- drawing board
- ruler
- triangle
- compass

A PROCEDURE TO FOLLOW

Draw the wrench according to these dimensions:

1. The wrench is 12" long with a center diameter of 7/16".
2. The two ends are 3/4" diameter and flattened on two sides to the thickness of the center (7/16").
3. There is a 1/2" square opening in each end.
   a. The square on one end is aligned so that two diagonal corners line up with the shaft of the wrench.
   b. The square on the other end is aligned so that two opposite sides of the square are perpendicular (at a 90° angle) to the shaft of the wrench.
4. Add the dimensions given to the appropriate parts of the wrench in your drawing.

WHAT DID YOU LEARN?

1. Compare your drawing to those of your classmates. Do all of the drawings look the same? Why or why not?

_____

_____

_____

2. What special skills do you think are needed to be able to make accurate technical drawings?

_____

_____

_____

LOGO DESIGN
Submitted by Charles H. Peteshel

Note to Teachers: *This activity can also be done on a computer, using a Draw or CAD program.*

DID YOU KNOW...?

Many companies have a logo (letters, symbols, or signs), which is used to identify the company. McDonalds has "Golden Arches," Nike has a "swoosh," and other companies have their own logos. Look around your classroom or lab. Look on books, machinery, even clothing for company logos. Companies often pay designers large sums of money to create these logos for them.

A PROBLEM TO SOLVE

The Samanski Boat & Hull Company has developed a new product that will require a logo. This product is a ski boat that will appeal to the young-at-heart individual who likes water sports. It will sell for $25,000. It is a prestige product. The logo that you design will appear on the bow of the boat and all sales literature. It must be rich looking and impressive, yet represent the product. Water should also be included in the design. The design will be no larger that 2-1/2 x 3 inches. BE CREATIVE!

RESOURCES YOU WILL NEED

A variety of tools such as
- pencil or pen
- paper (plain or graph)

- drawing board
- ruler
- compass
- triangles
- templates
- colored markers.

A PROCEDURE TO FOLLOW

1. Look at as many logos as possible for ideas.
2. Carefully reread the requirements under "A Problem to Solve"
3. Sketch some preliminary ideas. You can combine letters, symbols, and pictures. Use your creativity.
4. Draw your final design. Add color as desired.

WHAT DID YOU LEARN?

1. What did you think was the most difficult part of this activity?

_____

_____

What was the easiest part?

_____

_____

_____

2. Do you think you might be interested in a career as a designer? Why or why not?

_____

_____

_____

DRAWING FEATURES
Submitted by Charles H. Peteshel

DID YOU KNOW...?

When architects create a building design for a client, they include in the drawing many of the outdoor features that would be around the building in real life. Adding features such as plants, people, and vehicles makes the drawing more interesting and makes it easier to imagine how the building will actually appear.

A PROBLEM TO SOLVE

The drawing on the last page of this activity isn't as interesting as it would be if some outdoor features were included. Add shrubs, trees, sidewalks, people, vehicles, clouds, aircraft, or anything else that you think will enhance this drawing.

RESOURCES YOU WILL NEED

- pencil or pen
- paper
- drawing board
- ruler
- triangles
- compass
- templates

A PROCEDURE TO FOLLOW

1. Take a look at some buildings in your area. Notice the outdoor features such as shrubs, trees, fountain, and so on.
2. Study the building in the drawing on the next page. Imagine what outdoor features would make this building look especially good to a potential client.
3. Carefully draw in the features you have decided to include.

WHAT DID YOU LEARN?

1. Why do you think it's important to add plants outside buildings whenever possible?

_____

_____

_____

2. Adding features to a drawing of a building is one way an architect might try to "sell" a design. What are some other ideas an architect might use to make a building more interesting to a client?

_____

_____

_____

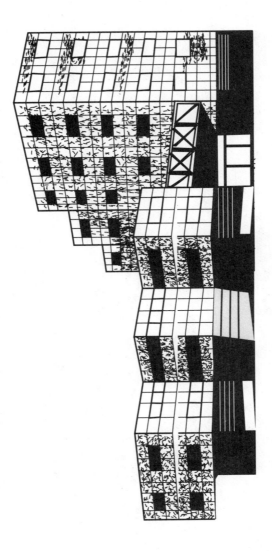

27

FLOOR PLAN
Submitted by Charles H. Peteshel

When an architect plans a home, there are several things that must be considered. The house must be big enough to meet the client's needs, it must be affordable, and it must be divided into areas for sleeping (bedrooms), living (living room), and service (kitchen, etc.).

A PROBLEM TO SOLVE

Devise a floor plan for a four-room home, one floor. A four-room home has been chosen so that you can get experience with a simplified design in order to learn the very basics of the floor plan.

RESOURCES YOU WILL NEED

- pencil or pen
- graph paper
- drawing board
- ruler
- triangles
- compass
- templates

A PROCEDURE TO FOLLOW

1. Check the floor plan example in your text on page 178.
2. Decide what rooms you want to include in your home.
3. Select the size for your four-room house.

4. Include symbols for doorways, windows, etc. in your drawing. Use the symbols shown in the example in your text.
5. Be neat and creative!

WHAT DID YOU LEARN?

1. What things must be considered when designing a home for a client?

_____

_____

_____

_____

2. Why is it important to make your drawing as neat as possible?

_____

_____

_____

_____

"CAN" THIS IDEA

Submitted by Dan Fouts

DID YOU KNOW...?

The board of directors of your soft drink company has just listened to the projected sales report from the marketing department—and it's not good. Your two main competitors have been outselling you over the last seven months. Something has to be done—and *soon*.

A PROBLEM TO SOLVE

The task of coming up with a new soft drink has been turned over to your R&D (research and development) department. The new drink is ready for production and distribution; all you need is an exciting name and design for the can.

RESOURCES YOU WILL NEED

- scratch paper
- 4-1/2" x 8-1/2" paper for final design
- pencil or pen
- colored markers
- one empty soda can
- tape

A PROCEDURE TO FOLLOW

1. You must work individually on this assignment.
2. Think of an exciting name for your new soft drink.

3. On the scratch paper, sketch three possible "eye-catching" designs. Remember: Visual impact (how attractive and appealing your design looks) will influence first-time buyers.
4. Select the best design and draw it FULL SIZE on the 4-1/2" x 8-1/2" paper.
5. In the design, be sure to include the ingredients, bar code, and canning authority (canned under authority of your name).
6. Bring in your own pop can and tape the finished label around it.
7. Submit for class evaluation.

WHAT DID YOU LEARN?

1. What shapes and colors seem to be the most eye catching?

_____

_____

_____

2. How might you change your design to make it even more appealing to consumers?

_____

_____

_____

INDIVIDUAL VS. MASS PRODUCTION

Submitted by Gary Fisher

DID YOU KNOW...?

There are two main ways of making products: (1) INDIVIDUAL PRODUCTION (making a product completely by yourself) and (2) MASS PRODUCTION (each step in the production process is done by a different person). This activity will explore these methods.

Your teacher will decide on a product to make. First, you will make the product completely by yourself. Then your entire class will make the product by mass production techniques. You will then compare these two forms of production.

RESOURCES YOU WILL NEED

• will vary depending on product chosen

PART 1 - Individual Production

A PROBLEM TO SOLVE

To make a product by individual production and to determine the time it takes to make the product.

A PROCEDURE TO FOLLOW

1. Determine the product you will produce.
2. Develop a plan of procedure (class input). FASTEN TO THIS ASSIGNMENT SHEET.

3. Each class member will make one product as per the plan of procedure. Monitor the time started and the time completed on a daily basis (use the Individual Production Time Sheet - Appendix I).

4. Identify your individual product by labeling.

5. Record your total minutes on this page and on the Master Data Sheet on the bulletin board.

   YOUR TOTAL PRODUCTION MINUTES_____

6. Use a calculator to determine the total class minutes as per the Master Data Sheet.

7. Using the formula below, find the average time (A) required to produce one product.

$$A \text{ (average time for one)} = \frac{T \text{ (total class minutes)}}{N \text{ (number produced)}}$$

A=

PART 2 - Mass Production

A PROBLEM TO SOLVE

To make enough products for the entire class by mass production and to determine the time it takes to make them.

A PROCEDURE TO FOLLOW

1. Determine your company name.

2. Develop a flow chart for production (class input—i.e., steps in the production process for the chosen product).

3. Your teacher will delegate job assignments (who will do which step in the production process).

4. Develop any fixtures needed and make a pilot run. ·

5. Begin mass production of your product (make one product for each class member) as per the flow chart.

NOTE: Monitor and record the group's daily working minutes on the Mass Production Time Chart (Appendix II).

6. Determine the average production time (A) per each product using the formula below.

$$A \text{ (average time for one)} = \frac{T \text{ (tot. min. x number of students)}}{N \text{ (number of units)}}$$

A =

WHAT DID YOU LEARN?

Answer these questions by placing an X on your choice.

	Individual	Mass
1. Which production was fastest?		
2. Which had best overall quality?		
3. Which did you enjoy the most?		

APPENDIX I - INDIVIDUAL PRODUCTION TIME SHEET

Day	Started	Stopped	Daily Minutes
1			
2			
3			
4			
5			
6			
7			
8			
9			
10			

Your total individual production minutes

APPENDIX II - MASS PRODUCTION TIME CHART

Day	Started	Stopped	Daily Minutes
1			
2			
3			
4			
5			
6			
7			
8			
9			
10			
Group's total mass production minutes			

PINHOLE PUZZLE

Submitted by Dan Fouts

DID YOU KNOW...?

After the research and development (R&D) department in a manufacturing company has determined an item to be manufactured, the information that has been gathered is sent to the design department. There, engineers decide the size, composition (what material it will be made of), shape, color, etc. of the new item. Often, a prototype, or handmade test model of the the item, is built.

A PROBLEM TO SOLVE

The CEO (chief executive officer) of your newly formed toy manufacturing company—Puzzles Я Us—has come to your unit with the lastest design. The cost of materials has already been determined, but he needs to know the length of time it takes to produce three prototypes. You have only three class periods and the limited resources listed below to work with. Make sure your team keeps an accurate record on the Operation Time Sheet.

RESOURCES YOU WILL NEED

- 1 piece of pine 3/4" x 3/4" x 15"
- 1 piece of 1/4" x 15" dowel
- 1 piece of abrasive paper
- drill presses
- electric hand drills
- disc sanders
- miter box saw
- back saws

- coping saws
- try squares
- combination squares
- ruler

DESIGN TEAM MEMBERS

_____

_____

_____

A PROCEDURE TO FOLLOW

1. Study the sketches at the end of this activity.
2. Notice that you need six blocks of wood and six dowels.
3. Carefully follow the criteria in the sketches to produce your puzzle.
4. Be careful to follow proper safety procedures when using the equipment!
5. Keep track of your time on the Operation Time Sheet.

OPERATION TIME SHEET				
STATION	ESTIMATED TIME	START	FINISH	ACTUAL TIME
Measuring Blocks				
Cutting Blocks				
Hole Drilling				
Dowel Cutting				
Sanding				
Assembly				
		TOTAL TIME		

WHAT DID YOU LEARN?

1. Why is neatness important in the appearance of the puzzle?

_____

_____

_____

2. Why is accuracy important in the construction of the puzzle?

_____

_____

_____

3. Why is it important to keep an accurate record of the time it took your team to produce the puzzle?

_____

_____

_____

4. How could your puzzle be improved?

_____

_____

_____

_____

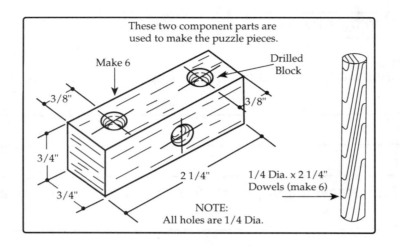

These two component parts are
used to make the puzzle pieces.

Make 6

Drilled
Block

3/8"

3/8"

3/4"

3/4"

2 1/4"

1/4 Dia. x 2 1/4"
Dowels (make 6)

NOTE:
All holes are 1/4 Dia.

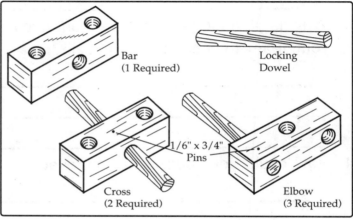

Bar
(1 Required)

Locking
Dowel

Cross
(2 Required)

1/6" x 3/4"
Pins

Elbow
(3 Required)

Solution to
Pin-Hole
Puzzle

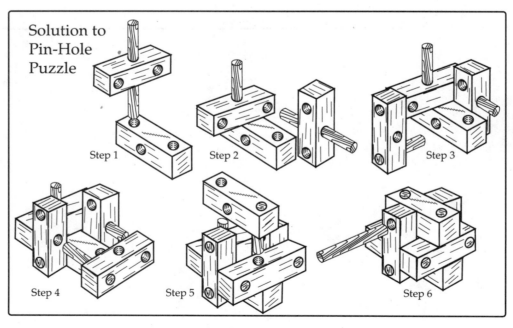

Step 1

Step 2

Step 3

Step 4

Step 5

Step 6

42

ALL BENT
OUT OF SHAPE

Submitted by Dan Fouts

DID YOU KNOW...?

The original paper clip was patented around 1900. Since that time there have been very few modifications (changes).

A PROBLEM TO SOLVE

You have just been informed that a rival company has developed a new paper clip design (shown below) to take over the market and put your firm out of business. You must work quickly and submit your best design—with four (4) alternate designs—to your boss by today.

Rival's Design

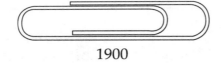

1900

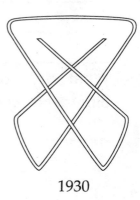

1930

RESOURCES YOU WILL NEED

- paper
- pencil or pen
- wire
- tape

A PROCEDURE TO FOLLOW

1. Sketch as many different paper clip configurations (shapes) as possible. <u>BE CREATIVE!!!</u>
2. Once you are finished, circle the <u>five</u> designs you like the most.
3. Select the one shape that you think will work the best.
4. Have your instructor approve your design. Obtain the wire.
5. Bend the wire into the final shape and tape it to your sketch sheet.

WHAT DID YOU LEARN?

1. Will your design hold more than one sheet of paper securely?

   _____

2. How many bends does it have?

   _____

3. Will the number of bends affect the cost to fabricate (make) the paper clip? (Explain why or why not.)

   _____

   _____

   _____

4. What did you do with the ends of the wire? Does it make a difference where they are? (Explain why or why not.)

   _____

   _____

   _____

5. Look at the three pictured paper clips and the amount of "surface area" and "contact points" they have to hold the papers. Does your design have more or less surface area and contact points? Will this affect its holding power? (Explain why or why not.)

   _____

   _____

   _____

WORLD'S TALLEST GOLF TEE

Submitted by Dan Fouts

DID YOU KNOW...?

Your research and engineering firm is in competition to design a new and revolutionary structural shape that can withstand heavy compression forces.   This structure must be inexpensive, easy to construct, and strong.

A PROBLEM TO SOLVE

Your Technology Challenge is to design and construct a free-standing newspaper tower that can support a golf ball as high as possible.

RESOURCES YOU WILL NEED

- three (3) full sheets of standard newspaper
- nine (9) inches of masking tape
- aliphatic resin glue or rubber cement
- cutting tool (not scissors)
- tape measure
- golf ball

A PROCEDURE TO FOLLOW

1. You and your partner will have 30 minutes to build your tower.
2. Think about your design before you start cutting. You might want to sketch a few ideas on paper.

3. Use necessary safety precautions when using the cutting tool.
4. A golf ball must be supported for 60 seconds at your tower's pinnacle.
5. The tallest structure wins the competition.
6. Measurements will be taken from the top of the golf ball to the floor.

GRADING CRITERIA: (Team Points)

_____ List the total height of the paper tower after the test.

_____ Calculate and list 1 point for every ten (10) inches of height.

WHAT DID YOU LEARN?

1. What factors caused some towers to be taller and sturdier than others?

_____

_____

_____

2. Do you consider your tower design to be a good one? Why or why not?

_____

_____

_____

3. What design changes would you make if you did this activity again?

_____

_____

_____

_____

Name_____ Date_____ Period_____

CUT - IT - OUT!

Submitted by Dan Fouts

DID YOU KNOW...?

Technology has been defined as a disciplined (meaning *planned*) process that uses scientific, material, and human resources to achieve human purposes. What this means is that we use what we have studied and learned from the natural world around us to develop materials and fashion tools to fulfill needs and make our lives more comfortable. This "process" is our major means of controlling, modifying, and adjusting to our environment. As mankind advances and continues to create more complex systems, we will need to expand our application of knowledge to also include the knowledge of application. (This means the ability to take information used in one way and apply it to a new situation in a creative and previously "unthought-of" manner.)

A PROBLEM TO SOLVE

The material "paper" comes in a wide variety of forms depending on how it is to be used (paper towels, tissue paper, etc.). You have each been given a half sheet of standard writing paper. You are to cut the paper any way you wish into one CONTINOUS STRIP, tape an end onto the floor, and then extend (stretch) the rest in one direction as far as possible without breaking it.

RESOURCES YOU WILL NEED

- one (1) sheet of paper 5-1/2" x 8-1/2"
- scissors
- one (1) piece of masking tape
- tape measure

A PROCEDURE TO FOLLOW

1. Cut your paper into one *continuous* strip.
2. If the strip breaks, the pieces cannot be fastened together.
3. Final distance is measured from the beginning point to where you are standing when the paper separates.

PERFORMANCE EVALUATION

TOTAL DISTANCE: _____ (in inches)

_____ (in feet)

10 to 15 feet = C
16 to 20 feet = B   Instructor's initials _____
21 feet and longer = A

WHAT DID YOU LEARN?

1. At what point did your paper break?

_____

2. What factors caused some designs to go farther than others?

_____

_____

_____

3. How could your design be changed to make it go farther?

_____

_____

_____

GO FOR THE GOLD
Submitted by Dan Fouts

DID YOU KNOW...?

While fishing off the Oregon coast, you and your friends discover a sunken pirate ship. The small cove you are in is only about 20" deep. Lying all around the wreck on the ocean floor are priceless gold bars. A massive hurricane, which will cover up all traces of your find, is due to strike the area in two days. You have only six hours of daylight and the resources on your boat to retrieve as many gold bars as possible.

A PROBLEM TO SOLVE

Pick up as many gold bars as you can in a five-minute time limit. You cannot get your hands wet. You must get the gold bars completely out of the water.

RESOURCES YOU WILL NEED

- scratch paper
- pencil or pen
- two balloons
- 8 straws
- up to 12" of tape
- cardboard
- up to 12" of wire
- one syringe
- 24" of plastic tubing
- three items of your choice

A PROCEDURE TO FOLLOW

1. Choose two partners to work with you on this activity.
2. Brainstorm some ideas for your gold retriever.
3. Decide on the best idea, keeping in mind the available resources.
4. Sketch a design of your idea.
5. Construct your gold retriever, using necessary safety precautions.
6. Make necessary adjustments.

WHAT DID YOU LEARN?

1. Is it easier or more difficult to develop creative ideas with a group rather than by yourself?   Why?

_____

_____

_____

_____

2. Why is it important to test your design after constructing it?

_____

_____

_____

_____

THE THROWAWAY THRONE

Submitted by Dan Fouts

DID YOU KNOW...?

In our lab, we have stools to sit on. Can you imagine sitting and relaxing on one of these in your living room for a long period of time? Or how about you and your family sitting around a table at a restaurant on them? All chairs must support the human form, but each—depending on its intended use—will vary widely in overall style, design, and appearance. From high chairs to recliners and bar stools to folding lawn chairs, we continue to adapt and modify one of the most basic and universally recognizable man-made shapes.

A PROBLEM TO SOLVE

The Monarch of Mongozia is to visit our school in eight days. The Monarch is a very fussy ruler and will not address the student body unless he has a proper "throne." We have been informed that the Monarch is a healthy man who weighs about 325 pounds. If the Monarch's throne does not hold his weight, it is a Mongozian custom for the builder of this throne to have his left ear removed from the side of his head and transplanted to the center of his forehead. (The Mongozian people know that any furniture builder with an ear on his forehead is not worth his weight in cardboard—the most highly prized material in their country.)

Your challenge is to design and construct a throne that will hold the Mongozian Monarch so that he will address the student body. A drawing with *full dimensions* and *construction details* will be required before the actual fabrication can begin.

RESOURCES YOU WILL NEED

- paper
- pencil or pen
- ruler
- cutting tools (craft knife, scissors, etc.)
- one (1) roll of masking tape
- cardboard boxes for appliances
- no glue, fasteners, or any other materials may be added

CONSIDERATIONS

STRENGTH	COMFORT (ergonomics)	ATTRACTIVENESS
load-bearing	seat/back pitch (angle)	proportions
stability	height	balance
connections	width	symmetry
	depth	

A PROCEDURE TO FOLLOW

1. Work with your team members to sketch a design of your throne.
2. Keep in mind the list of considerations.
3. Submit your drawing for approval. Be sure to include dimensions and construction details on your drawing.
4. Carefully construct your throne from cardboard.
5. Test your design for strength, comfort, and attractiveness.
6. Make necessary design changes.

WHAT DID YOU LEARN?

1. In this activity, what was the problem to be solved?

_____

_____

_____

2. What goals did your team set?

_____

_____

_____

3. Did you have alternative solutions?   What were they?

_____

_____

_____

4. How would you change your solution (design) next time?

_____

_____

_____

METEOR MADNESS

Submitted by Dan Fouts

Note to Students: *Your team of three technicians will have 15 minutes to complete this activity.*

DID YOU KNOW...?

As space exploration and planet colonization become more of a reality, we will need design structures and shelters that are light, strong, and easy to assemble.

A PROBLEM TO SOLVE

The year is 2023 and you have just been stationed on Titan, a moon of Saturn. Since there is no atmosphere and the moon passes daily through an asteroid belt, your first order of business is to quickly construct a shelter. This structure must be large enough to stand up in and strong enough to withstand the impact of a large, falling meteor.

RESOURCES YOU WILL NEED

- four (4) pieces of 8-1/2" x 11" paper
- two (2) brads
- up to 30 centimeters of string
- one (1) meter of masking tape
- one (1) research astronaut made from one length of pipe cleaner
- scissors

1. Consider structural shapes (tents, houses, commercial buildings, domes, etc.) and the strength of each.
2. Decide which shape would be most practical for your structure.
3. Construct your shelter. (Don't forget to include a door!)
4. Test your structure for strength.
5. Fashion your research astronaut out of pipe cleaner.

WHAT DID YOU LEARN?

1. Describe your design. State *why* your design should work.

_____

_____

_____

_____

_____

_____

SPACED OUT

Submitted by Dan Fouts

DID YOU KNOW...?

The year is 2012. An asteroid has smashed into your spacecraft, which was orbiting Neptune. The damage is extensive and only eight crew members are still alive.

A PROBLEM TO SOLVE

Your task is to rebuild the craft and limp back to Earth—two and a half years away.

CRITERIA

1. Four class periods will be allowed for rebuilding your spacecraft.
2. Spacecraft can have only one captain, so you must work alone on this challenge.
3. Build to scale of your choice: _____ = _____.
4. Your craft must have a cutaway or removable section for internal viewing.
5. Limitations
   A. Your spacecraft design must include the following:
      _____ sanitation   _____ sleeping
      _____ fuel   _____ food storage
      _____ recreation   _____ control center
      _____ food preparation   _____ water storage
   B. Your spacecraft must fit in one half of your locker.

RESOURCES YOU WILL NEED

- supplies from home (for example, egg cartons, pop/tin cans, toilet paper rolls, straws, toothpicks, etc.) Be creative!
- scrap wood
- necessary tools
- paper
- pencil or pen

A PROCEDURE TO FOLLOW

1. Sketch ideas for your design. Be sure to consider the limitations listed above.
2. Decide on the materials you will need to construct your design.
3. Collect needed materials.
4. Construct your spacecraft.

EVALUATION

☐ 10 points — Best design. To be voted by the class.
(will include top 10 of those voted on)

GRADE SCALE

☐ 40 points — Includes all design elements.

60 - 51	= A
50 - 41	= B
40 - 31	= C
30 - 21	= D

☐ 10 points — Correct scale and overall size.

WHAT DID YOU LEARN?

1. Why did you choose the design you used?

_____

_____

_____

_____

2. What feedback did you receive from your instructor and classmates?

_____

_____

_____

_____

3. How would you change your design next time? Why?

_____

_____

_____

_____

AIRPLANE FLIGHT CONTROL ACTIVITY
Submitted by Dennis Karwatka

DID YOU KNOW...?

As an airplane flies through the air, the pilot can control three types of motion. The plane can move up and down (*pitch*). It can move left and right (*yaw*). And it can roll clockwise or counterclockwise (*roll*).

The tail of an airplane has both a horizontal stabilizer and a vertical fin. Pitch is controlled by a moveable elevator on the horizontal stabilizer. Yaw in controlled by a moveable rudder on the vertical fin.

The wing of an airplane has moveable control surfaces along the trailing edge, near the tip. They are called *ailerons*, after the French word for wing tip. Ailerons work in pairs to control roll. When one is down, the other is up.

A PROBLEM TO SOLVE

At the turn of the century, many people were trying to build controllable engine-powered airplanes. Wilbur and Orville Wright were the first to succeed. The two young men conducted countless experiments. They invented and patented ailerons, which made it possible to control the flight of an airplane. Ailerons allow a plane to lean, or roll slightly. When an airplane makes a turn, it leans like a bicycle. It doesn't make a flat turn like a car. Without ailerons, it would have been almost impossible to fly an airplane.

Balsa wood gliders have only one adjustable flight control. You can slide the wing forward or back to change the flight characteristics. A forward setting is for loops and a rearward setting is for straight glides. However, balsa wood gliders have no elevators, rudders, or ailerons.

Your problem is to add elevators and ailerons to a glider and to make observations about the differences these additions make.

RESOURCES YOU WILL NEED

- small balsa wood glider
- two or three self-stick address labels
- fifty-foot tape measure, stopwatch, scissors

A PROCEDURE TO FOLLOW

The following should be done indoors if possible.
1. With wings at the rearward setting, fly the airplane and measure the maximum time of flight. Do it several times to get a good average. Figure the average by adding all of the times and dividing by the number of flights.
2. Fly the airplane several times and measure the maximum straight-line distance from where you launched it. Do it several times to get a good average.
3. Cut small pieces of label, about 3/16" x 1". Bend the pieces up along the one-inch length and remove them from the paper backing. Put one piece on top of each side of the horizontal stabilizer on the tail of the glider. They will be your elevator controls. Fly the glider to see what happens. (The glider should pitch upward.) Put the labels on the bottom side of the stabilizer and see what happens. (The glider should pitch downward.)
4. Remove the elevator controls and add a fresh piece of label for the rudder control on the vertical fin on the tail of the glider. Fly the glider to see what happens. When the label is placed on the right side, the plane should yaw to the right. With the label on the left side, the plane should yaw to the left.
5. Remove the rudder controls and make two fresh pieces of labels for the ailerons. Place one on the bottom side of the trailing edge

(back) of one wing and another on the top side of the other wing. Fly the glider to see what happens. (It should roll.) Reverse the controls and see if the glider rolls in the opposite direction.

WHAT DID YOU LEARN?

Have you ever heard the words *overcorrect* or *overcontrol*? They mean to use too much control. For example, suppose you were riding a bike and saw a hole in the street. If you turned the handlebars quickly, you might miss the hole, but you could overcorrect or overcontrol and lose control of the bike. That same thing might happen if you put in too much elevator control, for example. A small bend in the address label could have put the glider into a smooth climb. A larger bend could have made the aircraft quickly pitch upward and drop to the ground, out of control.

Real airplanes often use flight controls in combination. Rudder and ailerons together allow an airplane to lean during a turn. Rudder and elevator together allow a plane to make a turn while descending. Balsa wood gliders are very light and quite sensitive to aerodynamic drag. That's why you didn't fly the glider with combination controls. Sometimes, but not always, just one type of flight control puts so much drag on the glider that it flies strangely. Did that happen to you?

For more information on flight controls, look under the word *airplane* in your school's encyclopedia.

Name_____ Date_____ Period_____

MAGNETIC LEVITATION ACTIVITY

Submitted by Dennis Karwatka

DID YOU KNOW...?

A great deal of research is being conducted to develop a practical magnetic levitation (Maglev) train. Maglev trains have no wheels and do not make contact with the ground. A powerful magnetic force allows the train to float over the guide rails.

Ordinary trains have wheels that roll on metal rails. The rails keep the train pointed in the correct direction. Maglev trains have no wheels but operate along a *guideway*. The guideway acts like rails to keep the Maglev train on course.

Magnetic forces lift the train from the surface of the guideway. These same forces also propel the train forward. A series of individual electromagnets are located along the guideway. The electromagnets create a moving magnetic wave that carries the train along with it. The magnetic wave carries the train in much the same manner as a surfboard rider is carried by an ocean wave.

A PROBLEM TO SOLVE

You will build a Maglev vehicle from lightweight Styrofoam and use six electromagnets to lift it from the guideway. You will also use the electromagnets to move the vehicle forward or backward. A rotary switch will allow you to create a magnetic wave to sweep the vehicle along.

RESOURCES YOU WILL NEED

- six 5/16" x 2-1/2" inch bolts and nuts, and twelve flat washers
- enameled wire
- six-volt lantern cell battery
- rotary switch with at least six contacts
- 1" x 2" pine, 18" long
- two pieces 3/16" thick acrylic plastic, 1-3/4" x 18"
- Styrofoam cube, about 2" on a side
- glue, drill, drill bits, table saw

A PROCEDURE TO FOLLOW

(Note: There are several different detailed ways to assemble this Maglev vehicle. The procedure listed here is brief, and some specific decisions will be left to you.)

1. To get an idea of how make your Maglev vehicle, look at the assembly drawing, Figure 1 on the last page of this activity.

2. Arrange the washers and nuts on the six bolts as shown in Figure 2. Wrap them clockwise with the enameled wire to make six electromagnets. Leave at least three feet of wire free on the ends.

3. Use the table saw to cut slots for the plastic in the 1" x 2" pine board. Drill six 5/16" holes along the guideway. Start the first hole four inches from the end and then drill one every two inches.

4. Just barely screw the threaded ends of the electromagnets into the holes in the pine board. Place the acrylic plastic into the slots. Glue in place, if necessary. Continue screwing the bolts into the wood until the bolt heads are exactly as high as the plastic. See Figure 1 again.

5. Run the enameled wires along the guideway to the battery and rotary switch. Wire them according to the wiring guide in Figure 3. That is, for each electromagnet, one lead goes to the negative (-) terminal of the battery. Wire the other lead to the rotary switch in order: electromagnet 1 to the first connection, electromagnet 2 to

the second connection, and so on. Wire the common connection on the rotary switch to the positive (+) terminal of the battery.

6. Carve a lightweight vehicle out of Styrofoam, or glue one together. Glue the permanent magnet on the underside of the vehicle, as close as possible to the bolt heads.

7. Now it's time to test your Maglev system. Place your vehicle over electromagnet 1. Turn the rotary switch to the position 1 and see if your vehicle floats. If it's attracted to the electromagnet, reverse the permanent magnet.

8. Make the vehicle move by slowly rotating the rotary switch. You will create a magnetic wave that will carry your Maglev vehicle from one end of the guideway to the other.

WHAT DID YOU LEARN?

Turn the switch at different speeds to see how important a delicate touch can be. After a little practice, you'll soon be able to keep the vehicle floating smoothly as it moves.

Did you notice how difficult it was to stop the Maglev? One way is to shut off power to the magnets and have the vehicle contact the guideway. That is not very practical for a full-size train. Can you figure out why?

Try reversing the leads for one of the electromagnets on the end. It will then act as a brake to stop the vehicle before it goes whizzing off the end. That's the general technique used by Maglev trains.

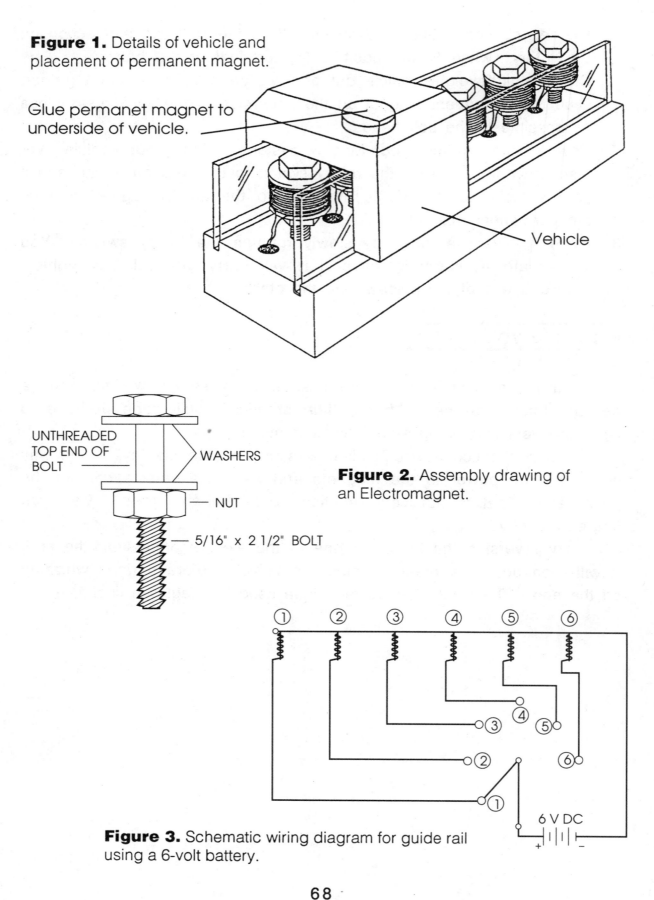

Figure 1. Details of vehicle and placement of permanent magnet.

Glue permanet magnet to underside of vehicle.

Vehicle

UNTHREADED TOP END OF BOLT

WASHERS

NUT

5/16" x 2 1/2" BOLT

Figure 2. Assembly drawing of an Electromagnet.

6 V DC

Figure 3. Schematic wiring diagram for guide rail using a 6-volt battery.

68

Name _____ Date _____ Period _____

WINGS AND THINGS

Submitted by Gary Fisher

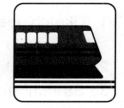

Note to Teachers: This activity is designed for groups of 2 to 3 students each. Three 45-minute periods may be required to complete this activity.

DID YOU KNOW...?

Wings, fins, and tails are critical to the performance of airplanes, rockets, and even race cars. For example, without the proper wing design, airplane engines could not lift the planes off the ground. This activity will explore the effects that "wings" and "things" have on an airborne projectile. Which shapes of fins are the best? What size is the best? Where is the best location for the wings? These are a few of the questions you will try to answer with this activity.

A PROBLEM TO SOLVE

Your group will "brainstorm" a method for propelling a balloon a *minimum* distance of 19 feet in a horizontal line. You will try to achieve the straightest, stablest, and fastest course possible.

RESOURCES YOU WILL NEED

- (5) medium balloons (must be the same size and shape)
- (2) manila file folders (or similar weight paper)
- (1) 20-foot piece of fishing line
- (1) 3-1/2 inch piece of drinking straw (large)
- (1) 3 foot piece of masking tape
- scissors, crayons or markers, ruler
- stopwatch or watch with second hand

A PROCEDURE TO FOLLOW

1. Sketch ideas for "fins," "wings," and "things" shapes. Layout design on manila folder(s) and cut out.
2. Thread straw piece onto fishing line.
3. Stretch and fasten fishing line (with straw) between two objects (at least 19 ft. apart).
4. Blow up balloon. (Do not tie closed—have one group member hold onto mouth of balloon. If the balloon is blown up too taught, adding the tape will cause it to burst.)
5. Attach balloon to the straw with tape. Attach "fins," "wings," and "things" and release.
6. Observe results of time trials. Test each design with three trials and average the results. Record average under Trial #1 on the chart on the next page.
7. Repeat steps (1) through (6) twice more, varying the wing and fin shapes and sizes.

Diagram of Procedure—the following is a simplified flow chart of the procedure for this activity:

1. Brainstorm and sketch ideas
   ↓
2. Layout and Cut
   ↓
3. Fasten to balloon
   ↓
4. Test
   ↓
5. Analyze and record results.
   ↓
6. Go back to Step 1 and repeat procedure twice more.

Use the chart on the next page to record the results of your trial runs.

Design no.	Trial #1	Trial #2	Trial #3	Average	Notes & Comments

WHAT DID YOU LEARN?

Discuss and answer the following questions as a group.

1. What were the characteristics of the "wings and things" that provided the fastest trial-run results?

_____

_____

_____

2. What were the characteristics of the "wings and things" that resulted in the slowest trial-run results?

_____

_____

_____

3. Did any other groups have similar results with similarly shaped "wings and things"?

_____

_____

_____

4. What general statement concerning the way wings and fins affect motion can your group make as a result of this activity?

_____

_____

_____

_____

_____

BOAT HULL DESIGN

Submitted by Dan Fouts

DID YOU KNOW...?

Boats and ships are designed with a hull shape determined by the purpose for the boat. For example, boats that are used to transport heavy loads often have flat bottoms for more stability. Look at the hull shapes below. Which shape do you think would be the most stable? Which shape looks like it would cut through the water the fastest?

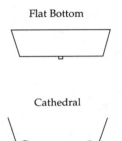

Flat Bottom

Round Bottom

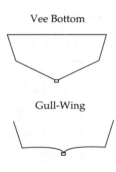

Vee Bottom

Cathedral

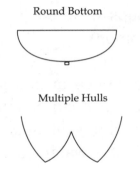

Multiple Hulls

Gull-Wing

A PROBLEM TO SOLVE

Build a boat that will travel at least 6 feet as fast as possible. The boat will float in a rain gutter full of water and a box fan will supply the energy.

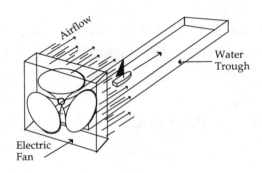

73

RESOURCES YOU WILL NEED

- 2" x 3-1/2" x 7" Styrofoam
- 7-1/2" straw
- glue
- one material of your choice from home
- popsicle sticks
- paper clips
- craft knife for shaping Styrofoam

A PROCEDURE TO FOLLOW

1. Four class periods will be allowed for design and construction of your boat.
2. Students will work in groups of three (must be someone you have not been with in a previous group).
3. Limitations
   - A fan must be the only source of power.
   - The boat must start from a dead start (no pushing, etc.).
4. Study the hull shapes in the sketches. Decide which shape would move the fastest through the water.
5. Carve the shape from your Styrofoam.
6. Design and make a sail for your boat.
7. Each member of the team must demonstrate the boat's operation.

WHAT DID YOU LEARN?

1. Will your boat travel at least six feet? (Six feet = 10 points, with 1 point for each additional foot up to 20 feet.)
2. Time will be worth points based on an average class time. The top 50% will receive 10 points; the lower 50% will receive 5 points.
3. Write a detailed technical paper worth 20 points. The paper should include the following.
   - what your boat is designed to do

- why you selected your hull design
- problems your design team had
- how you could have improved your design

4. Make detailed drawings worth 20 points.

GRADING SCALE

        60 - 50 = A
        49 - 40 = B
        39 - 30 = C
        29 - 20 = D

RUBBER BAND VEHICLE

Submitted by Dan Fouts

DID YOU KNOW...?

The Mayor of Bend has decided that in addition to the annual Cascade Cycling Classic there should be a Classic Car Competition—with a twist. The "car" can hold only one person and must be powered from the rubber of one truck tire inner tube.

A PROBLEM TO SOLVE

Your team's Technology Challenge is to produce a functional smaller scale prototype that must travel at least six feet.

RESOURCES YOU WILL NEED

- paper
- pencil or pen
- scrap wood
- 1/4" x 5" dowel rod (2 each)
- three rubber bands—your choice of size
- up to 24" of string
- three materials of your choice
- unlimited fasteners

A PROCEDURE TO FOLLOW

1. The rubber band must be part of the vehicle (no slingshots, etc.).
2. The vehicle must begin from a dead start (no throwing, etc.).

3. Each member of the team must demonstrate the vehicle in operation.
4. You must work with someone you have not worked with before.
5. Make a rough sketch of your design.
6. Make a final drawing.
7. Construct your vehicle.
8. Complete a Technical Data Report.

```
ROUGH SKETCH




```

```
FINAL SKETCH                                    approval _____




```

PERFORMANCE EVALUATION

Neatness = 5 points   _____

Travel: 6' = 10 points, with 1 point for each additional foot   _____

Travel accuracy: straight = 10 points; each foot off = -1 point _____

Technical Data Report: Must be filled out by each member
= 10 points   _____

TECHNICAL DATA REPORT

What the vehicle is designed to do:

_____

_____

_____

Construction sequence (1 point for each—correctly spelled):

_____   _____

_____   _____

_____   _____

_____   _____

_____   _____

Problems your team had and how you solved them:

_____

_____

_____

_____

Did the vehicle work and how could it be improved?

_____

_____

_____

_____

WHAT DID YOU LEARN?

1. Problem solving begins by identifying the problem. In this activity, what was the problem?

   _____

   _____

2. What goals did you set? What specifications did you have?

   _____

   _____

3. What alternative solutions did you come up with?

   _____

   _____

   _____

   _____

4. Why did you choose your solution?

   _____

   _____

5. What feedback did you receive? How would you change your solution for the next time?

   _____

   _____

   _____

6. Lubricants help reduce friction. Are there areas of your vehicle where you could apply lubricating compounds? What type of lubricant would you use?

_____

_____

_____

_____

7. Increasing the weight of parts of your vehicle may give you an advantage. How will this help? What vehicles are designed with weighted subsections?

_____

_____

_____

_____

_____

WINDSAIL TECHNOLOGY LEARNING PROJECT

Variable   A

Submitted   by   Gary   Fisher

Note to Teachers: This is the first of three 15-week projects. Each project can be done alone or in combination with the other two.

DID YOU KNOW...?

Wind is a type of energy. It can be used to create electricity by turning wind turbines which are connected to generators. Wind is also harnessed to provide various forms of locomotion (movement). Sail boards, ice-boats, and wind-powered wheeled vehicles are some popular uses for windpower.

In this project, we will be studying some basic concepts of wind power. Specifically, we will be studying windsails. Working in two- or three-person groups, your team will explore the effects of size of windsails on distance.

To be successful, you will need to study your project sheets and each appendix very carefully. Appendix IV contains some terms and definitions that will help you—study this sheet first.

Enjoy this project, and make it your mission to do things right!

A PROBLEM TO SOLVE

To compare distance versus the surface area of four windsails, each with a different surface area. (With the same wind force, how much further will a vehicle travel if you vary the size of its sail?)

RESOURCES YOU WILL NEED

- pine strips for sail frames and body struts - 1/8" x 1/8"
- pine strips for body - 3/16" x 3/16"
- 3/16" dowel rods
- hot glue w/gun
- plastic wrap for sail covering
- spray paint
- gum labels
- household fan
- sand paper
- prepared 2-inch acrylic wheels
- 1/8" dowel rods for axles

A PROCEDURE TO FOLLOW

1. Each team member will make a body as per drawing in Appendix I.
2. Team will make four (4) square sail frames with the following dimensions:
   a) 4" x 4" (frame for sail A)
   b) 6" x 6" (frame for sail B)
   c) 8" x 8" (frame for sail C)
   d) 10" x 10" (frame for sail D)

   Note: consider the thickness of frame wood when cutting pieces.
3. Team will attach a 3/16" dowel, using hot glue, to each sail frame as shown in Appendix II.
4. Team will sand and spray paint bodies and windsail frames.
5. Team will attach sail covering (plastic wrap) to sail frames using hot glue.
6. Team will neatly label the four sails A, B, C, D using the gum labels.
7. Team will select one body for testing purposes. (Important: Use this same body for all tests.)
8. Team will test their windsails for distance. Each windsail will run 4 times with results to be recorded on Data Sheet (Appendix III).

Compute average distance for each windsail. (Note: each team member must complete the Data Sheet.)

WHAT DID YOU LEARN?

Each team member will make a line graph showing the results of distance in feet traveled by each windsail. Use this graph to answer the following questions.

1. Which windsail was most efficient in utilizing the windpower?

_____

2. Which windsail was least efficient in utilizing windpower?

_____

3. Give possible reasons for your results.

_____

_____

_____

4. Compare your results with the other groups that did this project and discuss differences and similarities.

Differences _____

_____

_____

_____

Similarities _____

_____

_____

_____

EVALUATION

Each team member will submit:
  a. Windsail technology assignment sheet with completed questions
  b. Windsail vehicle and all sails
  c. Completed data sheet
  d. Line Graph

Evaluation:

What Did You Learn?_____(20)

Quality of body _____(20)

Quality of sails (group) _____(20)

Data Sheet_____(20)

Line Graph_____(20)

Total Points _____(100 possible)

APPENDIX I - BODY DETAILS

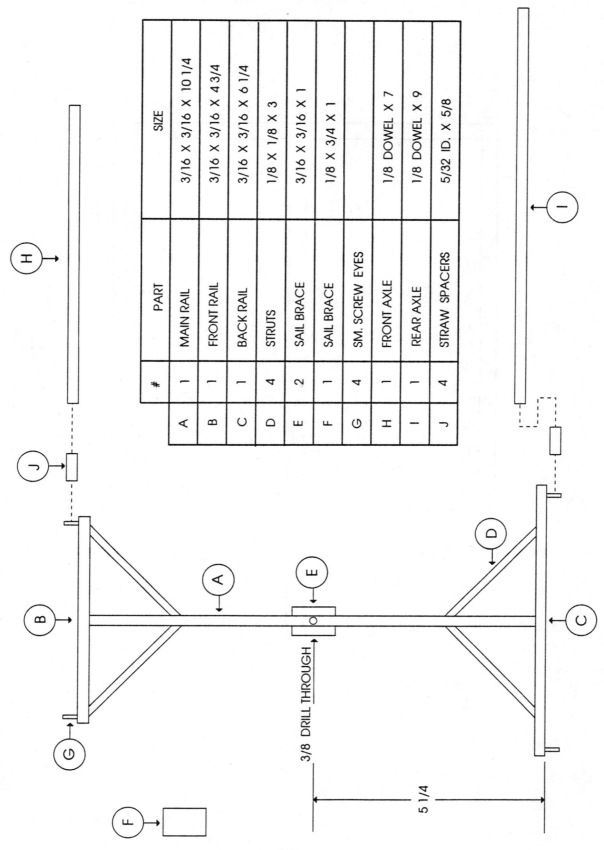

#		PART	SIZE
A	1	MAIN RAIL	3/16 X 3/16 X 10 1/4
B	1	FRONT RAIL	3/16 X 3/16 X 4 3/4
C	1	BACK RAIL	3/16 X 3/16 X 6 1/4
D	4	STRUTS	1/8 X 1/8 X 3
E	2	SAIL BRACE	3/16 X 3/16 X 1
F	1	SAIL BRACE	1/8 X 3/4 X 1
G	4	SM. SCREW EYES	
H	1	FRONT AXLE	1/8 DOWEL X 7
I	1	REAR AXLE	1/8 DOWEL X 9
J	4	STRAW SPACERS	5/32 ID. X 5/8

3/8 DRILL THROUGH

5 1/4

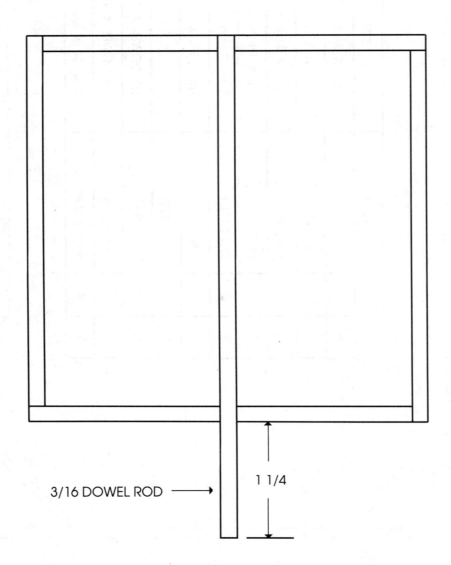

3/16 DOWEL ROD ⟶

1 1/4

APPENDIX III - DATA SHEET

This chart is for Raw Data in feet and inches.

SAIL	Run #1	Run #2	Run #3	Run #4
A				
B				
C				
D				

This chart is for data in feet.

SAIL	Run #1	Run #2	Run #3	Run #4	Average feet
A					
B					
C					
D					

Graph these figures

Terms Relating to This Unit:

Body   The base component of our vehicle that has four wheels and is designed to hold our sails.

Sail Covering   The covering component for the sail, which may consist of various materials.

Sail Frame   The component to which the sail covering is attached.

Windsail   A finished unit consisting of a sail frame and sail covering.   Many shapes are possible, but all are designed to harness wind as the source of power.

Construction Notes:

Band saw will be used for cutting frame segments to size while following the safety parameters.

X-Acto knives may be used to cut and shape pieces to the sail frames.   Note: Use caution during use or when carrying any sharp tool.

Hot glue gun used for all assembling operations.   Extra care is required to prevent hot glue from touching skin or clothing.

Drill press (3/16" bit)   to be used to drill hole in the body to allow for the sail attachment and removal from body. Note: remove rings and watches in addition to rolling up your sleeves when using drill press.

Hand drill (1/16" bit)   to be used to make pilot holes from screw eyes in axle assembly.

Safety glasses   to be worn at all times in the laboratory.

WINDSAIL TECHNOLOGY LEARNING PROJECT

Variable B

Submitted by Gary Fisher

Note to Teachers: This is the second of three 15-week projects. Each project can be done alone or in combination with the other two.

DID YOU KNOW...?

Wind is a type of energy. It can be used to create electricity by turning wind turbines which are connected to generators. Wind is also harnessed to provide various forms of locomotion (movement). Sail boards, ice-boats, and wind-powered wheeled vehicles are some popular uses for windpower.

In this project, we will be studying some basic concepts of wind power. Specifically, we will be studying windsails. Working in two- or three-person groups, your team will explore the effects of shapes of windsails on distance.

To be successful, you will need to study your project sheets and each appendix very carefully. Appendix IV contains some terms and definitions that will help you—study this sheet first.

Enjoy this project, and make it your mission to do things right!

A PROBLEM TO SOLVE

To compare distance versus the shape of four windsails, each with the same surface area. (With the same wind force, how much further will a vehicle travel if you vary the shape of its sail?)

- pine strips for sail frames and body struts - 1/8" x 1/8"
- pine strips for body - 3/16" x 3/16"
- 3/16" dowel rods
- hot glue w/gun
- plastic wrap for sail covering
- spray paint
- gum labels
- household fan
- 4 - 7" x 7" pieces of tag board or poster board for patterns
- sand paper
- prepared 2-inch acrylic wheels
- 1/8" dowel rods for axles

A PROCEDURE TO FOLLOW

1. Each team member will make a body as per drawing in Appendix I.
2. Team will make four sail frames each having an area of 49 square inches, and each being a different shape.
   (Note: Change the tag board to make templates for creating four different shapes of windsail frames. If you use all of the tag board surface area, each of your windsails will have a surface area of 49 square inches.
3. Team will attach a 3/16" dowel, using hot glue, to each sail frame as shown in Appendix II.
4. Team will sand and spray paint bodies and windsail frames.
5. Team will attach sail covering (plastic wrap) to sail frames using hot glue.
6. Team will neatly label the four sails A, B, C, D using the gum labels.
7. Team will select one body for testing purposes. (Important: Use this same body for all tests.)

8. Team will test their windsails for distance. Each windsail will run 4 times with results to be recorded on Data Sheet (Appendix III). Compute average distance for each windsail (Note: each team member must complete the Data Sheet.)
9. Neatly sketch your team's sail shapes above each letter.

A   B   C   D

WHAT DID YOU LEARN?

Each team member will make a line graph showing the results of distance in feet traveled by each windsail. Use this graph to answer the following questions.
1. Does windail shape effect the efficiency of sails?

_____

2. Which windsail shape was most efficient in utilizing the windpower?

_____

3. Which windsail shape was least efficient in utilizing windpower?

_____

4. Give possible reasons for your results.

_____

_____

_____

5. Compare your results with the other groups that did this project and discuss differences and similarities.

Differences _____

_____

_____

_____

Similarities _____

_____

_____

_____

EVALUATION

Each team member will submit:
    a. Windsail technology assignment sheet with completed questions
    b. Windsail vehicle and all sails
    c. Completed data sheet
    d. Line Graph

Evaluation:
    What Did You Learn?_____(20)

    Quality of body _____(20)

    Quality of sails (group) _____(20)

    Data Sheet_____(20)

    Line Graph_____(20)

    Total Points _____(100 possible)

APPENDIX I - BODY DETAILS

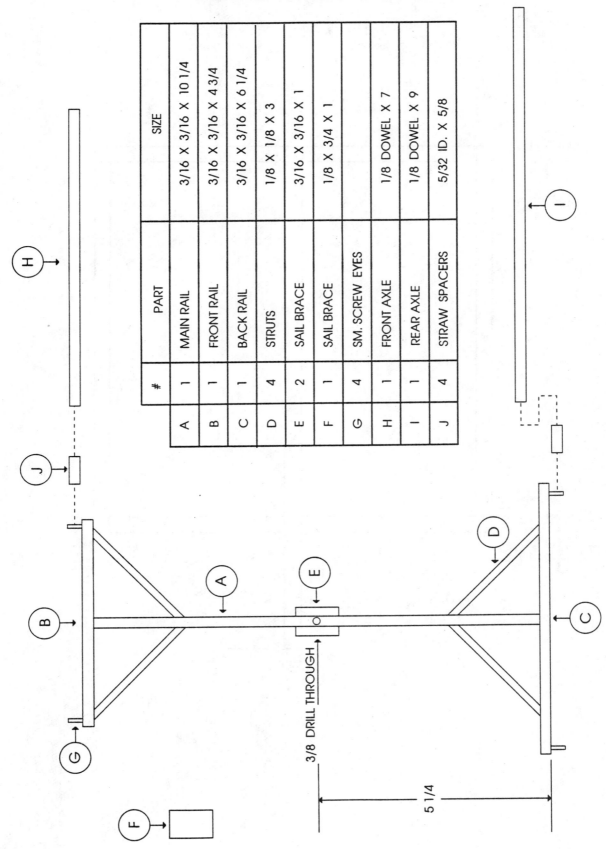

#	PART	SIZE
A	1	MAIN RAIL	3/16 X 3/16 X 10 1/4
B	1	FRONT RAIL	3/16 X 3/16 X 4 3/4
C	1	BACK RAIL	3/16 X 3/16 X 6 1/4
D	4	STRUTS	1/8 X 1/8 X 3
E	2	SAIL BRACE	3/16 X 3/16 X 1
F	1	SAIL BRACE	1/8 X 3/4 X 1
G	4	SM. SCREW EYES	
H	1	FRONT AXLE	1/8 DOWEL X 7
I	1	REAR AXLE	1/8 DOWEL X 9
J	4	STRAW SPACERS	5/32 ID. X 5/8

3/8 DRILL THROUGH

5 1/4

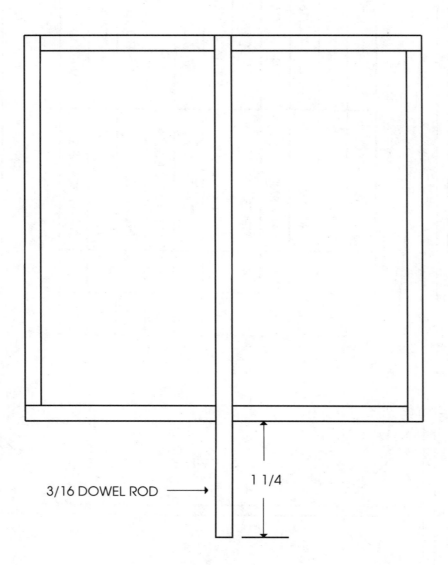

3/16 DOWEL ROD ⟶

1 1/4

APPENDIX III - DATA SHEET

This chart is for Raw Data in feet and inches.

SAIL	Run #1	Run #2	Run #3	Run #4
A				
B				
C				
D				

This chart is for data in feet.

SAIL	Run #1	Run #2	Run #3	Run #4	Average feet
A					
B					
C					
D					

Graph these figures

APPENDIX IV

Terms Relating to This Unit:

Body   The base component of our vehicle that has four wheels and is designed to hold our sails.

Sail Covering   The covering component for the sail, which may consist of various materials.

Sail Frame   The component to which the sail covering is attached.

Windsail   A finished unit consisting of a sail frame and sail covering.   Many shapes are possible, but all are designed to harness wind as the source of power.

Construction Notes:

Band saw will be used for cutting frame segments to size while following the safety parameters.

X-Acto knives   may be used to cut and shape pieces to the sail frames.   Note: Use caution during use or when carrying any sharp tool.

Hot glue gun used for all assembling operations.   Extra care is required to prevent hot glue from touching skin or clothing.

Drill press (3/16" bit)   to be used to drill hole in the body to allow for the sail attachment and removal from body.   Note: remove rings and watches in addition to rolling up your sleeves when using drill press.

Hand drill (1/16" bit)   to be used to make pilot holes from screw eyes in axle assembly.

Safety glasses   to be worn at all times in the laboratory.

WINDSAIL TECHNOLOGY LEARNING PROJECT

Variable C

Submitted by Gary Fisher

Note to Teachers: This is the third of three 15-week projects. Each project can be done alone or in combination with the other two.

DID YOU KNOW...?

Wind is a type of energy. It can be used to create electricity by turning wind turbines which are connected to generators. Wind is also harnessed to provide various forms of locomotion (movement). Sail boards, ice-boats, and wind-powered wheeled vehicles are some popular uses for windpower.

In this project, we will be studying some basic concepts of wind power. Specifically, we will be studying wind sails. Working in two- or three-person groups, your team will explore the effects of types of coverings on distance.

To be successful, you will need to study your project sheets and each appendix very carefully. Appendix IV contains some terms and definitions that will help you—study this sheet first.

Enjoy this project, and make it your mission to do things right!

A PROBLEM TO SOLVE

To compare distance versus the different sail coverings of four windsails. (With the same wind force, how much further will a vehicle travel if you vary the covering of its sail?)

RESOURCES YOU WILL NEED

- pine strips for sail frames and body struts - 1/8" x 1/8"
- pine strips for body - 3/16" x 3/16"
- 3/16" dowel rods
- hot glue w/gun
- sail covering materials (suggested):
    - plastic film
    - tissue paper
    - cotton fabric
    - open weave nylon (or the equivalent)
- spray paint
- gum labels
- household fan
- sand paper
- prepared 2-inch acrylic wheels
- 1/8" dowel rods for axles

A PROCEDURE TO FOLLOW

1. Each team member will make a body as per drawing in Appendix I.
2. Team will make four (4) square sail frames with the following dimensions:

    8" x 8"

    Note: consider the thickness of frame wood when cutting pieces.
3. Team will attach a 3/16" dowel, using hot glue, to each sail frame as shown in Appendix II.
4. Team will sand and spray paint bodies and windsail frames.
5. Team will attach four different types of sail covering to sail frames using hot glue.
6. Team will neatly label the four sails A, B, C, D using the gum labels.
7. Team will select one body for testing purposes. (Important: Use this same body for all tests.)

8. Team will test their windsails for distance. Each windsail will run 4 times with results to be recorded on Data Sheet (Appendix III). Compute average distance for each windsail (Note: each team member must complete the Data Sheet.)

WHAT DID YOU LEARN?

Each team member will make a line graph showing the results of distance in feet traveled by each windsail. Use this graph to answer the following questions.

1. Which windsail was most efficient in utilizing the windpower?

_____

2. Which windsail was least efficient in utilizing windpower?

_____

3. Give possible reasons for your results.

_____

_____

_____

4. Compare your results with the other groups that did this project and discuss differences and similarities.

Differences _____

_____

_____

_____

Similarities _____

_____

_____

_____

EVALUATION

Each team member will submit:
   a. Windsail technology assignment sheet with completed questions
   b. Windsail vehicle and all sails
   c. Completed data sheet
   d. Line Graph

Evaluation:

   What Did You Learn?_____(20)

   Quality of body _____(20)

   Quality of sails (group) _____(20)

   Data Sheet_____(20)

   Line Graph_____(20)

   Total Points _____(100 possible)

APPENDIX I - BODY DETAILS

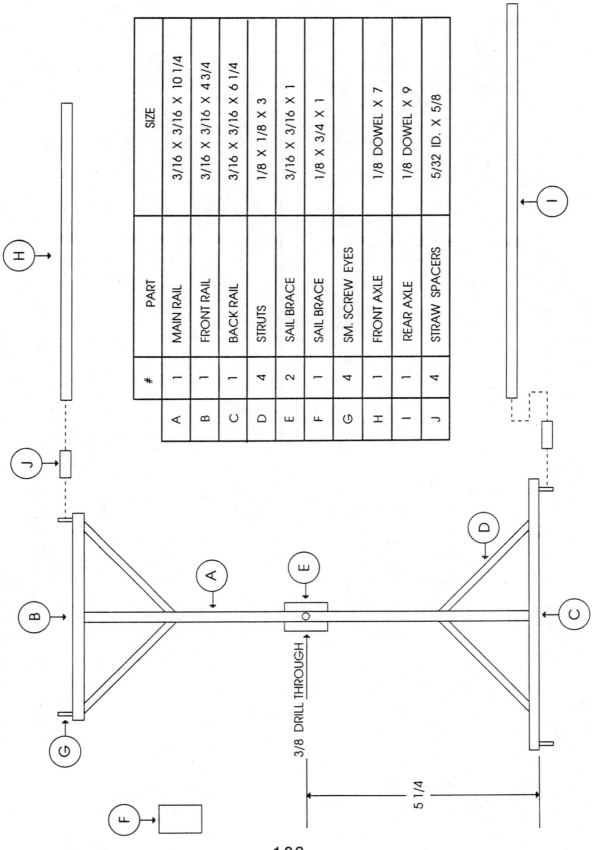

#		PART	SIZE
A	1	MAIN RAIL	3/16 X 3/16 X 10 1/4
B	1	FRONT RAIL	3/16 X 3/16 X 4 3/4
C	1	BACK RAIL	3/16 X 3/16 X 6 1/4
D	4	STRUTS	1/8 X 1/8 X 3
E	2	SAIL BRACE	3/16 X 3/16 X 1
F	1	SAIL BRACE	1/8 X 3/4 X 1
G	4	SM. SCREW EYES	
H	1	FRONT AXLE	1/8 DOWEL X 7
I	1	REAR AXLE	1/8 DOWEL X 9
J	4	STRAW SPACERS	5/32 ID. X 5/8

3/8 DRILL THROUGH

5 1/4

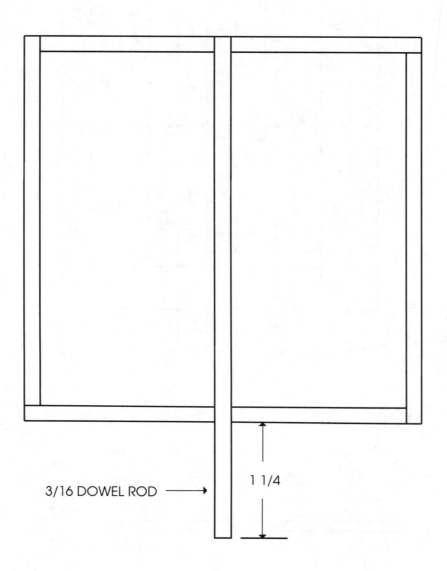

3/16 DOWEL ROD ⟶

1 1/4

APPENDIX III - DATA SHEET

This chart is for Raw Data in feet and inches.

SAIL	Run #1	Run #2	Run #3	Run #4
A				
B				
C				
D				

This chart is for data in feet.

SAIL	Run #1	Run #2	Run #3	Run #4	Average feet
A					
B					
C					
D					

Graph these figures

APPENDIX IV

Terms Relating to This Unit:

Body   The base component of our vehicle that has four wheels and is designed to hold our sails.

Sail Covering   The covering component for the sail, which may consist of various materials.

Sail Frame   The component to which the sail covering is attached.

Windsail   A finished unit consisting of a sail frame and sail covering. Many shapes are possible, but all are designed to harness wind as the source of power.

Construction Notes:

Band saw will be used for cutting frame segments to size while following the safety parameters.

X-Acto knives may be used to cut and shape pieces to the sail frames. Note: Use caution during use or when carrying any sharp tool.

Hot glue gun used for all assembling operations. Extra care is required to prevent hot glue from touching skin or clothing.

Drill press (3/16" bit) to be used to drill hole in the body to allow for the sail attachment and removal from body. Note: remove rings and watches in addition to rolling up your sleeves when using drill press.

Hand drill (1/16" bit) to be used to make pilot holes from screw eyes in axle assembly.

Safety glasses to be worn at all times in the laboratory.

SOLAR COOKER
Submitted by Jim Smallwood

DID YOU KNOW...?

Much of the earth's energy comes either directly or indirectly from the sun. Throughout history, people have turned to the sun to help fill energy needs. Unlike fossil fuels (coal, oil, natural gas) and uranium, sunlight is a renewable source of energy. Sunlight is abundant, dependable, and free, and as a fuel source it holds appeal because it is nonpolluting.

The potential of the sun's energy is unlimited. Despite this, however, very little of it is put to use directly. The reason for this is the difficulty in collecting widely scattered sunshine. Researchers and scientists will continue to experiment and discover new techniques for using solar energy.

A PROBLEM TO SOLVE

The purpose of this activity is to build a solar energy cooker. After the device has been constructed, you can put it to practical use by using the sun's rays for cooking.

RESOURCES YOU WILL NEED

- cardboard for constructing the base
- poster board for constructing the cooker
- fasteners (such as small nuts and bolts)
- glue and tape
- aluminum foil
- scissors
- dowel rod (1/16" or 1/8")

A PROCEDURE TO FOLLOW

1. With your teacher and class, discuss solar energy and the requirements for this assignment.
2. Your teacher may want to show you an example of a solar energy cooker.
3. Work in small groups of 2-3 students.
4. Construct the solar energy device following these directions:

   A. Construct the base using cardboard.

   Example:

   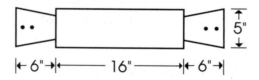

   B. Construct the cooker using poster board.

   Example:

   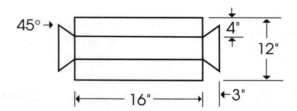

   C. Glue the aluminum foil to the front side of the cooker. Tape it on the backside.

   D. Fold the cooker and tape the sides together.

   E. Attach the cooker to the sides of the base with a fastener. A small nut and bolt will suffice.

Example:

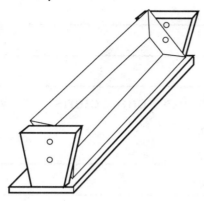   Or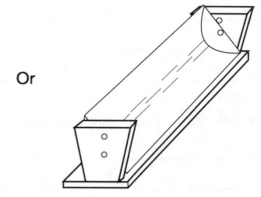

    F. Sharpen one end of the dowel rod and place it through the sides of the base like a skewer.

5. After completion, cook something (such as a hot dog) using the sun's rays.

6. Talk with your teacher about developing different cooker designs, cooking at different times during the day, or seeing how long it takes to cook on a cloudy day. Record data for any experiments you try.

7. As a group, present your discoveries to the class in a formal presentation. Or, develop a report and present the material to the teacher.

WHAT DID YOU LEARN?

1. Why is the sun such a wonderful resource to help meet our energy needs?

_____

_____

_____

2. If the sun's energy is such a wonderful energy resource, why is it not used to meet all our energy needs?

_____

_____

_____

3. What were some of the optimal cooking characteristics you discovered from your solar cooker activity?

_____

_____

_____

MR. WIZARD'S ELECTRIC MOTOR ACTIVITY

Submitted by Dennis Karwatka

DID YOU KNOW...?

There are many different ways of making a simple electric motor. The easiest was once shown on television by Don Herbert. To some people, Mr. Herbert is better known as "Mr. Wizard."

Mr. Wizard has been showing youngsters fascinating science experiments for many years. Your parents may have seen the *Mr. Wizard Show* when they were growing up. Today, some television stations carry *Mr. Wizard's World*. With his gentle, careful way of presenting technical principles, Mr. Wizard has influenced countless young adults to pursue careers in science, engineering, and technology.

Mr. Wizard's electric motor, like all electric motors, has two basic sections. One section is the rotating magnetic part called the *armature*. The other section is the stationary magnetic part called the *field*. When the motor is rotating, the armature produces a changing magnetic force that is attracted or repelled by the field. This attraction/repulsion keeps the motor rotating.

A PROBLEM TO SOLVE

In your home, heavy electric motors are used to operate washing machines and refrigerators. Medium electric motors are used in fans and vacuum cleaners. Light electric motors are used in tape players and toys.

The lightweight electric motor you will make will show you how the armature and field work together. It requires careful and delicate construction. You will have to pay careful attention to detail as you make and assemble the parts. Don't rush the job and you'll be pleased with the results.

RESOURCES YOU WILL NEED

- small permanent magnet
- 24" of enameled wire
- 24" of hookup wire
- 1-1/2 volt C or D battery
- two paper clips
- one small piece of Styrofoam plastic about 3/8" x 3/8" x 3/4"
- one large piece of 1" thick Styrofoam plastic about 3" x 3"
- masking tape, knife, wire cutters, pliers

A PROCEDURE TO FOLLOW

1. To get an idea of how to make your simple motor, look at the assembly drawing, Figure 1 on the last page of this activity.
2. Make the armature by wrapping the enameled wire ten times around the small piece of Styrofoam. Use pieces of tape to hold the wire in place. Leave about one inch of wire on each side. See Figure 2.
3. Use a knife to scrape *all* the enamel from one wire end. On the other wire end, scrape the enamel from only *one side.* The wire end with half the enamel removed will cause the armature to attract or repel the field as the armature spins.
4. Bend the paper clips and push them into the large piece of Styrofoam at points about two inches apart. Position the armature and make adjustments so that the armature is about 1/16" from the magnet. Be sure the armature is centered, well balanced, and can spin freely.
5. Cut two 6" pieces of hookup wire and remove the insulation from all four ends. Use the tape to make the battery and paper clip connections shown in Figure 1, but don't connect the wire to the bottom of the battery yet.

6. Your motor is now ready for its first run. Be sure everything looks OK and make that last electrical connection to the bottom of the battery. The armature will probably rotate slightly from side to side several times and then begin spinning. You can help it out by blowing gently on the armature.

WHAT DID YOU LEARN?

Mr. Wizard's motor usually works pretty well and it's fun. However, if you have some problems, check these points: (a) The armature must be as lightweight as possible and well balanced. (b) Make sure all wire connections are well made. (c) The magnet has to be reasonably strong and close to the armature. Try rotating it a quarter turn. (d) You can connect two or three batteries together to increase the electrical power.

Remember the wire end on which you removed only half the insulation? You did that so it could act as a switch as the armature rotates on the paper clips. That regular switching controls the electricity flowing to the wires in the armature. The armature is an electromagnet that is attracted or repelled by the permanent magnet. That attraction/repulsion keeps the motor spinning.

If you liked this motor activity, write to Mr. Wizard and tell him. His address is:

Mr. Don Herbert
Mr. Wizard's World
Nickelodeon Network
1515 Broadway Ave.
New York, NY 10036

Figure 1. Assembly Drawing

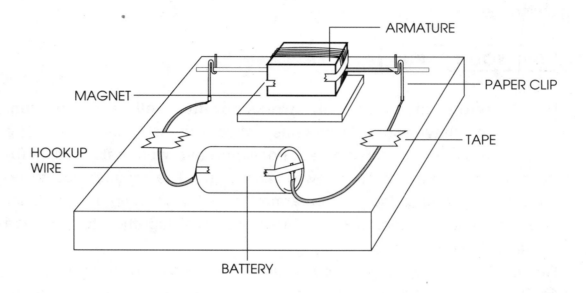

ARMATURE

MAGNET

PAPER CLIP

TAPE

HOOKUP
WIRE

BATTERY

Figure 2. Armature

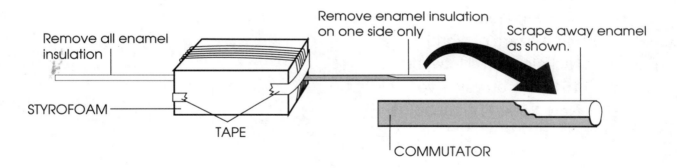

Remove all enamel
insulation

Remove enamel insulation
on one side only

Scrape away enamel
as shown.

STYROFOAM

TAPE

COMMUTATOR

114

Name_____ Date_____ Period_____

BALL LAUNCHER

Submitted by Dan Fouts

DID YOU KNOW...?

Energy that is stored is known as "potential energy." A stretched rubber band has enough potential energy to fly through the air for some distance. A boulder at the top of a hill also has great potential energy. As the boulder rolls down the hill or the rubber band flies through the air, the potential energy becomes "kinetic energy." Kinetic energy is energy in motion.

A PROBLEM TO SOLVE

Design and construct a device that will send a plastic ball into a wastepaper basket. The device must have a trigger mechanism. The basket will be set five feet away from the mechanism. You must get five balls into the basket in the fewest number of tries. The first attempt is practice and does not count. Your grade will be based on originality, neatness, construction techniques, accuracy, and the total number of shots required to get all five balls into the basket.

RESOURCES YOU WILL NEED

- scrap wood
- unlimited fasteners (nails, screws, paper clips, etc.)
- white glue
- up to 12" of 1/4" wooden dowel rod
- up to 12" of string
- any three materials of your choice
- scratch paper
- pencils or pens

A PROCEDURE TO FOLLOW

1. You will work in teams of three or four students.
2. Work together to sketch a design of your launcher. As you work, keep in mind that the launcher must incorporate a lever in its operation, it must sit flat on the table as it is operated (it cannot be thrown), and each team member must demonstrate its operation.
3. Carefully follow your design to construct your launcher.
4. Test the launcher for accuracy and range.

WHAT DID YOU LEARN?

1. How many attempts did it take to put five balls in the basket?

   _____

2. How could your design be improved?

   _____

   _____

   _____

HAND IT OVER!!!!
Submitted by Dan Fouts

DID YOU KNOW...?

More and more robots are being added to factory assembly lines each year in an effort to reduce construction time and costs while increasing quality and overall production. Robots are now capable of taking over many hazardous or repetitive tasks, such as spray painting and handling hot or radioactive materials. Since robots are capable of imitating many of the basic movements of humans, their uses in the future will certainly come to include applications in space technology, police work, home chores and scientific research.

A PROBLEM TO SOLVE

Problem solving in industry requires individuals to work as effective team members. In this activity, you will work as part of a team to design and manufacture a model robotic arm and gripping claw that must be operated by HYDRAULIC (fluid) power. When complete, your team's robot must be able to pick up and put down a small object, move it up and down, and move it to the left and to the right.

RESOURCES YOU WILL NEED

- paper
- pencil or pen
- six (6) syringes
- up to six (6) feet of aquarium tubing
- dowels and scrap wood
- assorted fasteners (glue, tape, screws, etc.)
- power equipment

A PROCEDURE TO FOLLOW

1. Sketch a design for your robotic arm and gripping claw.
2. Consider how the arm will move up and down and back and forth (on a swivel perhaps).
3. Work together with your team to construct your robotic arm.
4. Have your robotic arm evaluated.

PERFORMANCE EVALUATION

_____ 1. Gripping claw picks up four (4) marshmallows. (5 points for each)

_____ 2. Gripping claw holds the marshmallow throughout the entire travel distance. (5 points for each try)

_____ 3. Gripping claw gently sets down the marshmallow. (5 points for each try)

_____ 4. Robot arm moves up and down. (20 points)

_____ 5. Robot arm moves to the left and to the right. (20 points)

_____ TOTAL

WHAT DID YOU LEARN?

1. Describe how teamwork helped in the design of your robot.

_____

_____

_____

2. Describe one change that could be made to improve the way your team's robotic arm works.

_____

_____

_____

SURFACE SCIENCE TECHNOLOGY

DID YOU KNOW...?

Surface science is the study of materials that make contact with other materials. This includes liquid, solid, and gaseous materials. In fact, it includes nearly everything.

This science is used in the production of certain paints, detergents, printing inks, and rustproofing materials for cars. It is used to develop materials that will push pollutants such as oil across the surface of water. It is also used in biomedical devices such as Teflon™ coatings on artificial parts and extended-wear contact lenses.

You will use this science to experiment with the contact made between certain materials.

A PROBLEM TO SOLVE

Your task is to compare and analyze the adhering (sticking) and spreading characteristics of different materials on a solid and a liquid.

RESOURCES YOU WILL NEED

- 3 plate glass sheets or microscope slides
- silicone spray
- paraffin
- small container (4" x 4") to hold water
- mineral oil
- isopropyl (rubbing) alcohol
- denatured alcohol
- Dawn™ Dishwashing Liquid

- motor oil
- talcum powder
- eyedropper
- water
- Keri™ Lotion
- Teflon™-coated surface

1. Use a mild detergent to clean the glass sheets or slides. Rinse thoroughly. Wipe with isopropyl alchohol to assure that the surface is clean. Don't touch the cleaned surface; the oil from your skin will alter the test results.
2. Spray a light coating of silicone on one of the glass sheets.
3. Rub an even coating of paraffin on one of the glass sheets.
4. Leave the third glass sheet clean.
5. Place one drop each of denatured alcohol, mineral oil, and water on the clean glass sheet. Be sure the drops don't touch each other. Determine the contact angle for each of the three liquids by eyeing the bubble formed on the surface of the glass sheet. Use the examples that follow to help you decide the angle. Record the results on the Data Sheet.

6. Repeat step 5 using the silicone-coated glass surface, the paraffin-coated glass surface, and the Teflon™-coated surface. Record your results on the Data Sheet.
7. Fill the small container with tap water. Lightly coat the surface of the water with talcum powder.
8. Place one or two drops of isopropyl alcohol on the surface of the water. Record the results on the Data Sheet.
9. Repeat steps 7 and 8 using Keri™ Lotion, Dawn™ Dishwashing Liquid, and mineral oil. Be sure to record your results after each test.
10. Use what you learned in steps 8 and 9 to clean an oil slick. Put fresh water in the small container. Place a few drops of motor oil on the surface of the water. Experiment with the alcohol,

dishwashing liquid, lotion, and mineral oil to determine which material is most effective in moving the oil across the surface of the water.

WHAT DID YOU LEARN?

1. Which materials seemed to spread rather than bead up?

   _____

   _____

2. Did any material react totally different on any of the glass surfaces?

   _____

   _____

3. Were the results of the isopropyl alcohol long-lasting? Why?

   _____

   _____

4. Did the Keri™ Lotion and mineral oil obtain the same results?

   _____

   _____

5. Why did the Keri™ Lotion outperform the mineral oil?

   _____

   _____

6. What materials caused the talcum powder to move to the side of the container?

   _____

   What materials caused the motor oil to be moved to the side of the container?

   _____

7. How could materials that cause things to move on the surface of water be used to contain something like an oil slick?

_____

_____

_____

_____

DATA COLLECTION SHEET

Liquids on Solids

1. Record the contact angles of liquids placed on a clean glass surface.

   denatured alcohol _____

   mineral oil _____

   water _____

2. Record the contact angles of liquids placed on a glass surface with a coating of silicone.

   denatured alcohol _____

   mineral oil _____

   water _____

3. Record the contact angles of liquids placed on a glass surface with a coating of paraffin.

   denatured alcohol _____

   mineral oil _____

   water _____

4. Record the contact angles of liquids placed on a Teflon™-coated surface.

   denatured alcohol _____

   mineral oil _____

   water _____

Liquids on Liquids

1. What action took place when these materials were placed on the talcum powder covering the water in the dish?

   isopropyl alcohol _____

   Keri™ Lotion _____

Dawn™ Dishwashing Liquid _____

_____

mineral oil _____

SINGLE-PARENT PLANTS

DID YOU KNOW...?

Pollination and fertilization are necessary for sexual reproduction to take place in plants. Often, the pollen will be carried from a different plant by an insect or a bird. This is called *cross-pollination*. In the same way that a child is different from its parents, the resulting plant is different from each of its "parents."

There is only one parent in asexual reproduction, and the resulting offspring (in this case, a plant) is identical to the parent. A plant that comes from a single parent is called a *clone*. The process is often called *cloning*.

Cloning is often done to make new plants with the same color flower as the parent plant. Sexual reproduction would probably change the color of the flower.

Plants are cloned in many ways. Tip cutting is one popular method. In this process, a piece of the parent plant's stem is cut off, rooted, and planted in its own container.

A PROBLEM TO SOLVE

You have a plant with a flower of a color that has never been seen before. How can you reproduce the plant so that you can sell the unusually colored flowers?

RESOURCES YOU WILL NEED

- box or flat
- plastic wrap

- vermiculite to half fill the box (a mixture of 50% peat moss and 50% coarse sand can be substituted)
- rooting hormone (available in plant stores)
- sharp knife
- pencil
- water
- light source (flourescent light or a window)
- plant (geraniums, philodendron, chrysanthemum, Christmas cactus, fuschia, and lantana work well)

A PROCEDURE TO FOLLOW

1. Half fill the box with vermiculite.
2. Evenly moisten the vermiculite and pat with your hand to make it firm.
3. Cut the plant at a node, the point where a leaf is attached to the stem, from a nonflowering shoot. The cuttings should be 3" to 5" long.
4. Pinch off the lowest leaves on the cuttings.
5. Wet the bottom inch of the stems and dip in the rooting hormone.
6. Use a pencil to make holes in the vermiculite.
7. Insert the bottom 1"-2" of the stems into a pencil hole and firm the vermiculite around them so they will stand.
8. Cover the box with plastic wrap. Poke air holes in the cover.
9. Place the box 6" below a flourescent light or in front of a window that is bright but that does not receive direct sunlight.
10. After the cuttings have rooted (usually a few weeks), replant them in 3" pots.

WHAT DID YOU LEARN?

1. What are some advantages and disadvantages of asexual reproduction?

_____

_____

_____

_____

2. Why are some plants cloned?

_____

_____

_____

_____